PRAYERS IN POETRY

PRAYERS IN
POETRY

Compiled by
W. BERTRAM WHITE

UNIVERSITY OF LONDON PRESS LTD
WARWICK SQUARE, LONDON E.C.4

Printed & Bound in England for the UNIVERSITY OF LONDON PRESS, LTD.,
by HAZELL WATSON & VINEY LTD., Aylesbury and Slough

Preface

MOST of us have a deep desire to know and love God better and to have an ever-increasing faith in His goodness and loving kindness to mankind.

We know that prayer is the link which binds us to God, who has created us and given us all the innumerable blessings of life, but when we try to speak to Him in prayer we find difficulty in expressing our thoughts and conveying just what we want to say to Him. Consequently, unless we make up our minds to keep on trying, we are apt to be discouraged or to repeat the same few prayers we have learned over and over again.

In this book there are prayers to be used for many occasions. Thus among others are included morning and evening prayers, prayers of thanksgiving for all God's goodness, prayers for relatives and friends, prayers for health and fitness and the power to persevere, and graces to be said before and after meals.

Many of the prayers being in poetic form, it is not only easier to read and learn them, but, the poets having expressed their thoughts in the choicest language, they possess an added inspiration.

It is hoped that the readers of these prayers will be drawn closer to God and that their lives will be spiritually enriched.   W.B.W.

Acknowledgments

FOR permission to use the following copyright poems in this book the compiler and publishers wish to express their thanks to:

Messrs. Evans Brothers Ltd. for "Look Down on Me" by J. Kirby, and "Grace and Thanksgiving" by Elizabeth Gould; Mrs. Knowles for the poem "O Jesus, Once a Child" by the late Adeline White; Messrs. Faber & Faber Ltd. for "A Child's Prayer" by Siegfried Sassoon; Messrs. William Heinemann Ltd. for "Prayer for Gentleness to All Creatures" by John Galsworthy from *The Collected Poems of John Galsworthy*; the Oxford University Press for an extract from the hymn "Son of God, Eternal Saviour" by S. C. Lowry, and for three verses of the hymn "For the Beauty of the Earth" by F. S. Pierpoint, by permission of the Estate of the late F. S. Pierpoint; Miss Erica Oxenham for an extract from "A Little Te Deum of the Commonplace" by John Oxenham; Miss D. E. Collins, Mrs. G. K. Chesterton's executrix, for the poem "How Far is it to Bethlehem?" by Frances Chesterton; Messrs. Thomas Nelson & Sons Ltd. for "Children's Prayer" by Albert D. Watson from *Poets Calling*; the Oxford University Press for Canon G. W. Briggs' verse "Our Father, for our Daily Bread" from *Songs of Praise* (Enlarged Edition); Messrs. Basil Blackwell & Mott Ltd. for the poem "Evening Song" by Edith King; Miss Stella Mead for her poem "If I had Lived in Bethlehem"; Messrs. William Blackwood & Sons Ltd. for the poem "In Bethlehem" by Alfred Noyes from *Collected Poems*; and Miss M. Louise Haskins for an extract from "The Gate of the Year".

In certain cases it has not been possible to trace copyright holders, but the publishers will be pleased to make full acknowledgment of any rights not acknowledged here in subsequent editions of this book.

Contents

8

The Creator's Praise

From all that dwell below the skies
Let the Creator's praise arise:
Let the Redeemer's name be sung
Through every land by every tongue.

ISAAC WATTS

Father, We Thank Thee

Father, we thank Thee for the night
And for the pleasant morning light,
For rest and food and loving care,
And all that makes the world so fair.
Help us to do the thing we should.
To be to others kind and good,
In all we do, in all we say,
To grow more loving every day.

Thanks to Spring

We thank Thee, Heavenly Father,
　For all the lovely spring,
For primroses and bluebells,
　And little birds that sing.

For woods and fields to play in,
　For bright blue sky and sea,
For everything we thank Thee.
　All beauty comes from Thee.

MARY ANDERSON

Look Down on Me

Look down on me, a little one,
Whose life on earth is but begun:
  Dear Saviour, smile on me.

Watch over me from day to day,
And when I work, or when I play,
  Dear Saviour, smile on me.

Help me to do Thy holy will,
With lovely thoughts my mind to fill:
  Dear Saviour, smile on me.

J. KIRBY

O Jesus, Once a Child

O Jesus, once a child like me!
Teach me how to grow like Thee.

Teach me always how to be
Wise and strong and kind like Thee.

May I learn to know and find
Love and goodness in my kind.

O Jesus, once a child like me!
Teach me how to grow like Thee.

ADELINE WHITE

The Morning Bright

The morning bright,
  With rosy light,
Has waked me up from sleep;
  Father, I own,
  Thy love alone
Thy little one doth keep.

  All through the day,
  I humbly pray,
Be Thou my Guard and Guide;
  My sins forgive,
  And let me live,
Blest Jesus, near Thy side.

THOMAS O. SUMMERS

As in Heaven, Thy Will be Done

Thro' the night Thy angels kept
Watch above me while I slept,
Now the dark has passed away,
Thank Thee, Lord, for this new day.

North and south and east and west
May Thy holy name be blest;
Everywhere beneath the sun,
As in Heaven, Thy will be done.

WILLIAM CANTON

A Spring Prayer

For flowers that bloom about our feet;
For tender grass, so fresh, so sweet;
For song of bird, and hum of bee;
For all things fair we hear or see,
Father in heaven, we thank Thee!

RALPH W. EMERSON

For Thy Name's Sake

O Lord God,
Make me to hear Thy loving-kindness in the morning,
    For in Thee is my trust;
Shew Thou me the way that I should walk in,
    For I lift up my soul unto Thee.
Teach me to do the thing that pleaseth Thee,
    For Thou art my God;
Let Thy loving Spirit lead me forth into the land of
                           righteousness;

    For Thy Name's sake.

from Psalm cxliii

Day by Day

I desire, O God, this day
   most earnestly to please Thee.
   What I do, make me do, simply as Thy child.
   Let me be throughout the day as a child in his loving
      Father's presence, ever looking up to Thee.
   May I love Thee for all Thy love.

May I thank Thee, if not in words, yet in my heart, for
      such gift of love, for each comfort which Thou
      allowest me day by day.

EDWARD BOUVERIE PUSEY

A Child's Prayer

For Morn, my dome of blue,
For Meadows green and gay,
And Birds who love the twilight of the leaves,
Let Jesus keep me joyful when I pray.

For the big Bees that hum
And hide in bells of flowers;
For the winding Roads that come
To Evening's holy door
May Jesus bring me grateful to His arms,
And guard my innocence for evermore.

SIEGFRIED SASSOON

My Morning Star

My voice shalt Thou hear in the morning,
  For the shadows have passed away,
And out from the dark like a joyous lark,
  My heart soars up with the day;
And its burden all is blessing,
  And its accent all is song,
For Thou hast refreshed its slumber
  And Thy strength hath made it strong.

My voice shalt Thou hear in the morning,
  For the day is all unknown,
And I am afraid without Thy aid,
  To travel its hours alone.
Give me Thy light to lead me,
  Give me Thy hand to guide,
Give me Thy living presence,
  To journey side by side.

Star of eternal morning,
  Sun that shall ne'er decline,
Day that is bright with unfading light,
  Ever above me shine.
And the day shall all be noontide,
  And the night shall vanish far,
When my path of life is guided
  By that bright and morning star.

Christ! Once Thyself a Boy

Christ! once Thyself a boy,
   Our boyhood guard and guide;
Be Thou its light and joy,
   And still with us abide,
That Thy dear love, so great and free,
   May draw us evermore to Thee.

W. WALSHAM HOW

The Knight's Prayer

God be in my head,
  And in my understanding;

God be in mine eyes,
  And in my looking;

God be in my mouth,
  And in my speaking;

God be in my heart,
  And in my thinking;

God be at my end,
  And at my departing.

from *Sarum Primer*

A Prayer for Gentleness

To all the humble beasts there be,
To all the birds on land and sea,
Great Spirit, sweet protection give
That free and happy they may live!

And to our hearts the rapture bring
Of love for every living thing;
Make us all one kin, and bless
Our ways with Christ's own gentleness!

JOHN GALSWORTHY

God Make My Life

God make my life a little light
    Within the world to glow,
A little flame that burneth bright,
    Wherever I may go.

God make my life a little flower
    That giveth joy to all,
Content to bloom in native bower,
    Although the place be small.

God make my life a little song
    That comforteth the sad,
That helpeth others to be strong
    And makes the singer glad.

God make my life a little staff
    Whereon the weak may rest,
That so what health and strength I have
    May serve my neighbours best.

God make my life a little hymn
    Of tenderness and praise;
Of faith that never waneth dim
    In all His wondrous ways.

MATILDA BETHAM-EDWARDS

A Prayer for Fitness

Holy God, who madest me
And all things else to worship Thee;
Keep me fit in mind and heart,
Body and soul to take my part.
Fit to stand, fit to run,
Fit for sorrow, fit for fun,
Fit to work and fit to play,
Fit to face life day by day:
Holy God, who madest me,
Make me fit to worship Thee.

A Prayer for Grace to Persevere

Jesu, good above all other,
Gentle Child of gentle mother,
In a stable born our Brother,
   Give us grace to persevere.

Jesu, cradled in a manger,
For us facing every danger,
Living as a homeless stranger,
   Make we Thee our King most dear.

Jesu, for Thy people dying,
Risen Master, death defying,
Lord in Heaven, Thy grace supplying,
   Keep us to Thy Spirit near.

Lord, in all our doings guide us,
Pride and hate shall ne'er divide us;
We'll go on with Thee beside us,
   And with joy we'll persevere!

PERCY DEARMER

God's Tokens

If I should find some lonely person doubting
The wondrous tales of old—
I'd bid him see the lilac bushes blooming
Or watch a leaf unfold.

I'd show the soft red feathers of a robin,
The night moth's powdered wings,
A star, a glow-worm, ripples on the water—
A thousand other things.

MARGARET WYMER

O Lord, My Strength, and My Redeemer

Let the words of my mouth,
  and the meditation of my heart,
Be acceptable in Thy sight,
  O Lord, my strength, and my redeemer.

from Psalm xix

Lord of Light

Lord of light, whose name outshineth
  All the stars and suns of space,
Deign to make us Thy co-workers
  In the kingdom of Thy grace;
Use us to fulfil Thy purpose
  In the gift of Christ Thy son:
Father, as in highest heaven
  So on earth Thy will be done.

H. ELVET LEWIS

For the Beauty of the Earth

For the beauty of the earth,
  For the beauty of the skies,
For the love which from our birth
  Over and around us lies:
    Gracious God, to Thee we raise
    This our sacrifice of praise.

For the beauty of each hour
  Of the day and of the night,
Hill and vale, and tree and flower,
    Sun and moon and stars of light:

For the joy of human love,
  Brother, sister, parent, child,
Friends on earth, and friends above,
  For all gentle thoughts and mild:
    Gracious God, to Thee we raise
    This our sacrifice of praise.

F. S. PIERPOINT

May We for Others Live

As Thou, Lord, hast lived for others
  So may we for others live;
Freely have Thy gifts been granted,
  Freely may Thy servants give.
Thine the gold and Thine the silver,
  Thine the wealth of land and sea,
We but stewards of Thy bounty,
  Held in solemn trust for Thee.

S. C. LOWRY

Glad that I Live am I

Glad that I live am I:
  That the sky is blue;
Glad for the country lanes,
  And the fall of dew.

After the sun the rain,
  After the rain the sun;
This is the way of life,
  Till the work be done.

All that we need to do,
  Be we low or high,
Is to see that we grow
  Nearer the sky.

LIZETTE WOODWORTH REESE

I Will Give Thanks

For the comforting warmth of the sun that my body
    embraces,
For the cool of the waters that run thro' the shadowy
    places,
For the balm of the breezes that brush my face with their
    fingers,
For the vesper hymn of the thrush when the twilight
    lingers,
Now with a breath that is deep-drawn, breath of a heart
    without care,
I will give thanks and adore Thee, God of the open air!

HENRY VAN DYKE

Vesper

Go with us as Thy House we leave;
By Thee our homes be blest;
Where e'er we gather present be,
Good angels guard our rest.

Teach us to serve Thee through the week;
Thoughts, words, and deeds direct;
Move us to love Thy creatures all;
From evil things protect!

FREDERICK WARREN

We Thank Thee, Lord

We thank Thee, Lord, for this fair earth,
The glittering sky, the silver sea;
For all their beauty, all their worth,
Their light and glory, come from Thee.

Thanks for the flowers that clothe the ground,
The trees that wave their arms above,
The hills that gird our dwellings round,
As Thou dost gird Thine own with love.

Yet teach us still how far more fair,
More glorious, Father, in Thy sight,
Is one pure deed, one holy prayer,
One heart that owns Thy Spirit's might.

BISHOP GEORGE COTTON

Prayer for Loved Ones

All our loved ones we commend
Lord, to Thee, man's truest friend:
Guard and guide them to the end,
We beseech Thee, Jesus.

Prayer for Absent Friends

Holy Father, in Thy mercy,
Hear our anxious prayer;
Keep our loved ones, now far distant,
'Neath Thy care.

Father, Son, and Holy Spirit,
God the One in Three,
Bless them, guide them, save them, keep them
Near to Thee.

I. S. STEPHENSON

Let Us Give Thanks

For all the first sweet flushings of the Spring;
The greening earth, the tender heavenly blue;
The rich brown furrows gaping for the seed;
For all Thy grace in bursting bud and leaf,—

. . . .

For hedgerows sweet with hawthorn and wild rose;
For meadows spread with gold and gemmed with stars;
For every tint of every tiniest flower;
For every daisy smiling to the sun;
For every bird that builds in joyous hope;
For every lamb that frisks beside its dam;
For every leaf that rustles in the wind;
For spiring poplar, and for spreading oak;
For queenly birch, and lofty swaying elm;
For the great cedar's benedictory grace;
For earth's ten thousand fragrant incenses,—
Sweet altar-gifts from leaf and fruit and flower;
For every wondrous thing that greens and grows;
For widespread corn,—billowing golden seas;
For rippling stream, and white-laced waterfall;
For purpling mountains; lakes like silver shields;
For white-piled clouds that float against the blue;
For tender green of far-off upland slopes;

. . . .

For all we see; for all that underlies,—
We thank Thee, Lord!
From *A Little Te Deum of the Commonplace*
JOHN OXENHAM

Grace and Thanksgiving

We thank Thee, Lord, for quiet upland lawns,
For misty loveliness of autumn dawns,
For gold and russet of the ripened fruit,
For yet another year's fulfilment, Lord,
      We thank Thee now.

For joy of glowing colour, flash of wings,
We thank Thee, Lord; for all the little things
That make the love and laughter of our days,
For home and happiness and friends, we praise
      And thank Thee now.

ELIZABETH GOULD

Let Everything that hath Breath Praise the Lord

All that we see rejoices in the sunshine,
  All that we hear makes merry in the Spring:
God grant us such a mind to be glad after our kind,
      And to sing
    His praises evermore for everything.

Much that we see must vanish with the sunshine,
  Sweet Spring must fail, and fail the choir of Spring:
But Wisdom shall burn on when the lesser lights are
    gone,
      And shall sing
    God's praises evermore for everything.

CHRISTINA ROSSETTI

For Joys of Service

For joys of service, Thee we praise,
Whose favour crowneth all our days;
For humble tasks that bring delight,
When done, O Lord, as in Thy sight,
Accept our offerings, Lord most high,
Our work, our purpose sanctify,
And with our gifts may we have place,
Now in the Kingdom of Thy grace.

How Far is it to Bethlehem?

How far is it to Bethlehem?
    Not very far.
Shall we find the stable-room
    Lit by a star?

Can we see the little Child?
    Is He within?
If we lift the wooden latch
    May we go in?

May we stroke the creatures there—
    Ox, ass, or sheep?
May we peep with them and see
    Jesus asleep?

If we touch His tiny hand,
    Will He awake?
Will He know we've come so far
    Just for His sake?

Great kings have precious gifts,
    And we have naught;
Little smiles and little tears
    Are all we brought.

For all weary children
    Mary must weep;
Here, on His bed of straw,
    Sleep, children, sleep.

God in His mother's arms,
    Babes in the byre,
Sleep, as they sleep who find
    Their heart's desire.

FRANCES CHESTERTON

What Shall I Sing?

Sing, sing, what shall I sing?
Christmas is coming, with every good thing;
Christmas is coming with music and mirth;
Heralding joy to the ends of the earth.

Rhyme, rhyme, what shall I rhyme?
Singing-boys carolling, belfries a-chime;
Choirs in the churches, and waits in the snow,
Telling the tidings of long, long ago.

Praise, praise, what shall I praise?
Christmas, this sweet and most blessed of days,
Offering all the world over again
Happiness, peace, and goodwill towards men.

ELIZABETH FLEMING

If I had Lived in Bethlehem

If I had lived in Bethlehem
  When Mary's Babe was born,
I could have seen Him on the hay,
  That first Christmas morn.

I would have knelt down on the floor,
  And for my morning prayer
Said, "Gentle Jesus, meek and mild,"
  While He was lying there.

I might have walked along the road
  And met the Three Wise Men
With gold and frankincense and myrrh,
  If I'd been living then.

STELLA MEAD

He Came All So Still

He came all so still
  Where His mother was,
As dew in April
  That falleth on the grass.

He came all so still
  To His mother's bower,
As dew in April
  That falleth on the flower.

He came all so still
  Where His mother lay,
As dew in April
  That falleth on the spray.

Mother and maiden
  Was never none but she;
Well may such a lady
  God's mother be.

O Holy Child of Bethlehem

O holy Child of Bethlehem,
    Descend to us, we pray;
Cast out our sin, and enter in,
    Be born in us to-day.
We hear the Christmas Angels
    The great glad tidings tell:
O come to us, abide with us,
    Our Lord Emmanuel.

PHILLIPS BROOKS

The Lamb

Little lamb, who made thee?
 Dost thou know who made thee?
Gave thee life, and bade thee feed,
 By the stream, and o'er the mead;
Gave thee clothing of delight,
Softest clothing, woolly, bright;
Gave thee such a tender voice,
Making all the vales rejoice?
 Little lamb, who made thee?
 Dost thou know who made thee?

 Little lamb, I'll tell thee,
 Little lamb, I'll tell thee,
He is callèd by thy name,
For He calls Himself a Lamb.
He is meek, and He is mild;
He became a little child.
I a child, and thou a lamb,
We are callèd by His name.
 Little lamb, God bless thee!
 Little lamb, God bless thee!

WILLIAM BLAKE

O Lamb of God

O Lamb of God,
that takest away the sins of the world,
    Have mercy on us.
Thou that takest away the sins of the world,
    Have mercy on us.
Thou that takest away the sins of the world,
    Receive our prayer.
Thou that sittest at the right hand of God the Father,
    Have mercy on us.

from *Gloria in Excelsis*

Christ Be With Me

Christ be with me, Christ within me,
Christ behind me, Christ before me,
Christ beside me, Christ to win me,
Christ to comfort and restore me,
Christ beneath me, Christ above me,
Christ in quiet, Christ in danger,
Christ in hearts of all that love me,
Christ in mouth of friend and stranger.

from St. Patrick's Breastplate

He Prayeth Best

He prayeth well, who loveth well
    Both man and bird and beast,
He prayeth best, who lovest best
    All things both great and small;
For the dear God who loveth us,
    He made and loveth all.

SAMUEL TAYLOR COLERIDGE

Hear, O Heavenly Father,
Hear Us

Hear, O Heavenly Father, hear us,
   While our voices rise to Thee:
Saviour, guide us and be near us,
   Help us all to follow Thee.

When the robes of night enfold us,
   May we feel that Thou art near;
May Thy loving hand still hold us
   Though the day is shining clear.

In life's battles, Lord, defend us,
   May we true and faithful be;
We will go where Thou dost send us,
   We will try to be like Thee.

ALBERT D. WATSON

Grace Before Meals

1

Here a little child I stand
Heaving up my either hand;
Cold as paddocks though they be,
Here I lift them up to Thee,
For a benison to fall
On our meat and on us all.

ROBERT HERRICK

2

Thank You for the world so sweet,
Thank You for the food we eat,
Thank You for the birds that sing—
Thank You, God, for everything!

3

Our Father, for our daily bread
Accept our praise and hear our prayer.
By Thee all living souls are fed;
Thy bounty and Thy loving care
With all Thy children let us share.

G. W. BRIGGS

4

May God bless what His bounty hath provided
Through Jesus Christ our Lord.

5

Great God, Thou giver of all good
Accept our praise, and bless our food;
Grace, health, and strength to us afford
Through Jesus Christ, our risen Lord.

Grace After Meals

1

We thank Thee, Lord, for this our food,
But more because of Jesu's blood.
Let manna to our souls be given—
The Bread of Life sent down from heaven.

2

For these and all other mercies
We bless God's holy name
Through Jesus Christ our Lord.

3

To God, who gives our daily bread
　A thankful song we raise,
And pray that He who sends us food
　May fill our hearts with praise.

4

Praise God, from whom all blessings flow;
Praise Him, all creatures here below;
Praise Him above, ye heavenly host;
Praise Father, Son, and Holy Ghost.

BISHOP KEN

Red Geraniums

Life did not bring me silken gowns,
Nor jewels for my hair,
Nor sight of gabled, foreign towns
In distant countries fair,
But I can glimpse beyond my pane a green and friendly
hill,
And red geraniums aflame upon my window-sill.

The brambled cares of every day,
The tiny, humdrum things
May bind my feet when they would stray,
But still my heart has wings
While red geraniums are bloomed against my window-
glass,
And low above my green-sweet hill the gipsy wind-
clouds pass.

And if my dreamings ne'er come true,
The brightest and the best,
But leave me love my journey through,
I'll set my heart at rest,
And thank Thee, God, for home-sweet things, a green
and windy hill,
And red geraniums aflame upon my window-sill.

MARTHA HASKELL CLARK

To-day

So here hath been dawning
  Another blue day:
Think, wilt thou let it
  Slip useless away?

Out of eternity
  This new day is born;
Into eternity,
  At night, will return.

Behold it aforetime
  No eye ever did:
So soon it for ever
  From all eyes is hid.

Here hath been dawning
  Another blue day:
Think, wilt thou let it
  Slip useless away?

THOMAS CARLYLE

Winter

'Tis winter now; the fallen snow
Has left the heavens all coldly clear;
Through leafless boughs the sharp winds blow,
And all the earth lies dead and drear.

And yet God's love is not withdrawn;
His life within the keen air breathes;
His beauty paints the crimson dawn,
And clothes the boughs with glittering wreaths.

And though abroad the sharp winds blow,
And skies are chill, and frosts are keen,
Home closer draws her circle now,
And warmer glows her light within.

. . . .

O God! who giv'st the winter's cold,
As well as summer's joyous rays,
Us warmly in Thy love enfold,
And keep us through life's wintry days.

SAMUEL LONGFELLOW

We Thank Thee Then, O Father

We thank Thee then, O Father,
  For all things bright and good;
The seed-time and the harvest,
  Our life, our health, our food.
No gifts have we to offer
  For all Thy love imparts,
But that which Thou desirest,
  Our humble, thankful hearts.

JANE M. CAMPBELL

Blessed Be the Lord God

Blessed be the Lord God who only doth wondrous
   things.
And blessed be His glorious name for ever:
And let all the whole earth be filled with His glory;
            Amen, and Amen.

from *Psalm lxxii*

A Grateful Heart

Thou who hast given so much to me,
Give one thing more, a grateful heart.

GEORGE HERBERT

O Worship the Lord

Give unto the Lord glory and strength.
Give unto the Lord the glory due unto His name.
O worship the Lord in the beauty of holiness.

from *Psalm xcvi*

In Bethlehem

A child was born in Bethlehem, in Bethlehem,
in Bethlehem.
The wise men came to welcome him: a star stood
o'er the gable;
And there they saw the King of Kings, no longer
thronged with angel wings,
But croodling like a little babe, and cradled in
a stable.

ALFRED NOYES

Out in the Fields

The little cares that fretted me,
  I lost them yesterday,
Among the fields above the sea,
  Among the winds at play,
Among the lowing of the herds,
  The rustling of the trees,
Among the singing of the birds,
  The humming of the bees.
The foolish fears of what might pass
  I cast them all away
Among the clover-scented grass,
  Among the new-mown hay,
Among the hushing of the corn,
  Where drowsy poppies nod,
Where ill thoughts die and good are born—
  Out in the fields with God.

The Life and Light

Thou art, O God, the life and light
Of all this wondrous world we see;
Its glow by day, its smile by night,
Are but reflections caught from Thee;
Where'er we turn, Thy glories shine,
And all things fair and bright are Thine.

THOMAS MOORE

O God, Who Art the Light

O God, who art the light of the minds that know
  Thee,
The life of the souls that love Thee,
The strength of the wills that seek Thee,
Help us so to know Thee
That we may truly love Thee,
So to love Thee that we may fully serve Thee
Whose service is perfect freedom.

ST. AUGUSTINE

The Country Faith

Here in the country's heart,
　　Where the grass is green,
Life is the same sweet life
　　As it e'er hath been.

Trust in a God still lives,
　　And the bell at morn
Floats with a thought of God
　　O'er the rising corn.

God comes down in the rain,
　　And the crop grows tall—
This is the country faith,
　　And the best of all!

NORMAN GALE

We Give Thee Thanks, O Lord

We give Thee thanks, O Lord,
    Who hast preserved us through the day.
We give Thee thanks,
    Who wilt preserve us through the night.
Bring us in safety, we beseech Thee, O Lord,
    to the morning hours,
That Thou mayest receive our praise at all times;
    through Jesus Christ our Lord.

       Gelasian, translated by WILLIAM BRIGHT

I Will Magnify Thee

I will magnify Thee, O God my King:
    And I will praise Thy Name for ever and ever:
Every day will I give thanks unto Thee,
    And praise Thy Name for ever and ever.

       from *Psalm cxlv*

Evening Song

Soft falls the night,
The day grows dim,
To Thee I lift my evening hymn,
O Lord of dark and light.

My hands I raise,
A little spire,
And send my voice up high and higher
To Thee in happy praise.

For home and friend,
For books and toys,
For all the countless loves and joys
That Thou dost daily send.

Close Thou mine eyes,
That when the day
Returns once more from far away,
I may rejoicing rise.

EDITH KING

O Give Thanks

O give thanks to Him who made
Morning light and evening shade.
Source and giver of all good,
Nightly sleep and daily food,
Quickener of our wearied powers,
Guard of our unconscious hours.

JOSEPH CONDER

A Prayer for Safety

Lord, keep us safe this night,
    Secure from all our fears;
May angels guard us while we sleep,
    Till morning light appears.

Good Night

Good night! Good night!
Far flies the light;
But still God's love
Shall shine above,
Making all bright,
Good night! Good night!

VICTOR HUGO

The Good Shepherd

The Lord is my shepherd; I shall not want.

He maketh me to lie down in green pastures:

He leadeth me beside the still waters.

He restoreth my soul:

He leadeth me in the paths of righteousness for His name's sake.

Yea, though I walk through the valley of the shadow of death,

I will fear no evil: for Thou art with me;

Thy rod and Thy staff they comfort me.

Thou preparest a table before me in the presence of mine enemies:

Thou anointest my head with oil; my cup runneth over.

Surely goodness and mercy shall follow me all the days of my life:

And I will dwell in the house of the Lord for ever.

Psalm xxiii

I Will Lift Up Mine Eyes
Unto the Hills

I will lift up mine eyes unto the hills, from whence cometh my help.

My help cometh from the Lord, which made heaven and earth.

He will not suffer thy foot to be moved: He that keepeth thee will not slumber.

Behold, He that keepeth Israel shall neither slumber nor sleep.

The Lord is thy keeper: the Lord is thy shade upon thy right hand.

The sun shall not smite thee by day, nor the moon by night.

The Lord shall preserve thee from all evil: He shall preserve thy soul.

The Lord shall preserve thy going out and thy coming in from this time forth, and even for evermore.

Psalm cxxi

The Lord's Prayer

Our Father, which art in Heaven,
Hallowed be Thy name;
Thy kingdom come;
Thy will be done,
On earth as it is in heaven.
Give us this day our daily bread.
And forgive us our trespasses,
As we forgive them that trespass against us.
And lead us not into temptation,
But deliver us from evil!
For Thine is the kingdom,
The power and the glory,
For ever and ever.
    Amen.

The Lord's Name Be Praised

The Lord's Name be praised
from the rising of the sun unto the going down of the
    same.
    Blessed be the Name of the Lord
from this time forth for evermore.

from *Psalm cxiii*

The Gate of the Year

I said to the man who stood at
   the gate of the year:
Give me a light that I may tread
   safely into the unknown. And he replied:
Go out into the darkness and put your hand
   into the hand of God.
That shall be to you better than light
   and safer than a known way.

M. L. HASKINS

Index of First Lines